HANNAH

Illustrated by Gordon Stowell

Every summer Hannah and her husband, Elkanah, and their friends got ready for a long journey.

They left their homes high in the hills and travelled to a very special church in a town called Shiloh.

Each year there was a big harvest festival at the church. Hundreds of people came. It was like a holiday.

But Hannah felt very sad. She had no children.

"Don't worry," said her husband.
"I love you."

Hannah went by herself to the
church. There she prayed,
"Dear God, please let me have a
baby." She told Eli, the priest,
and he prayed for her.

One day Hannah had some
wonderful news. "I'm going to have
a baby," she said to everyone.
The baby was born and she called
him Samuel.

After a few years Hannah took Samuel to Eli, the priest. "I want him to stay here and help you," she said.

This was Hannah's way of saying thank you to God.

Every year Hannah came to see Samuel and she took him a new coat.

One year Samuel said to his mother, "In the middle of the night I heard a voice calling 'Samuel, Samuel'."

"I hurried to Eli, but Eli hadn't called me. The voice came again. It was God. He wanted to speak to me."

When Hannah heard this she knew that God loved Samuel, and had a special job for him. Hannah and Elkanah had five more children and they were very happy.

You can read about Hannah in the Old Testament. It is in the First book of Samuel, chapter 1, and chapter 2, verses 18 to 21.

Little Fish Book

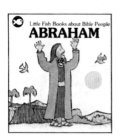

Little Fish Books about Bible People
ABRAHAM

Little Fish Books about Bible People
RUTH

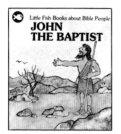

Little Fish Books about Bible People
JOHN THE BAPTIST

Little Fish Books about Bible People
PETER